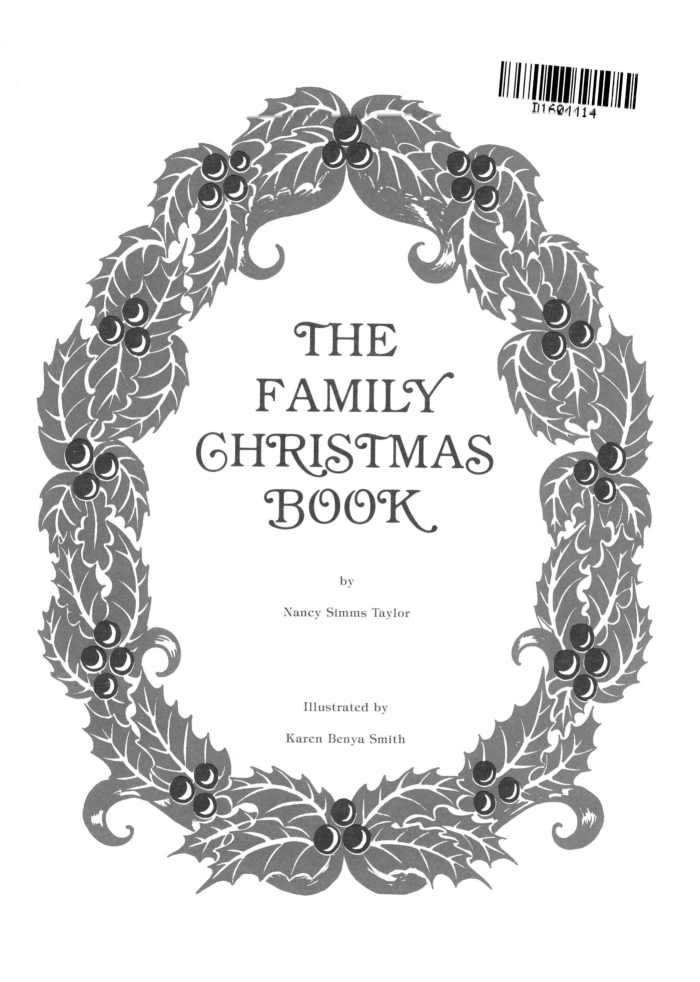

THE FAMILY CHRISTMAS BOOK

by

Nancy Simms Taylor

Illustrated by

Karen Benya Smith

Christmas Memories

of the

_____

Family

Keep this family Christmas Book
Faithfully through the years.
Record your Christmas memories,
The love and the good cheer.

When twenty-five years have come and gone
Won't it be a pleasure,
To have this book to cherish
As your special Christmas Treasure.

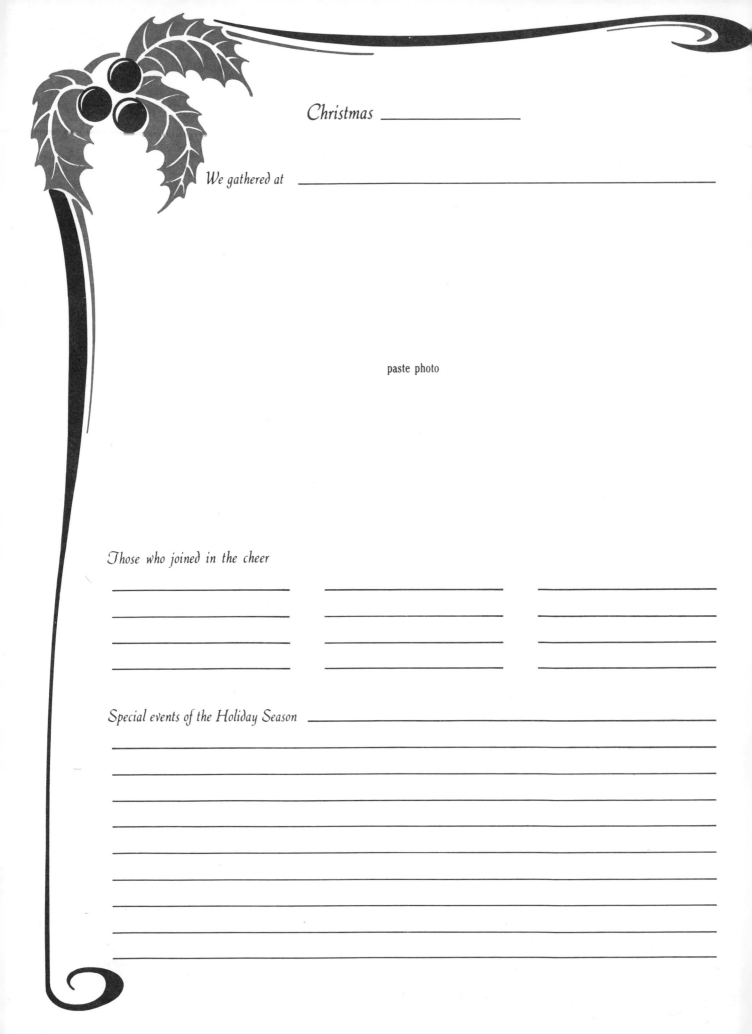

Christmas _____

We gathered at _____

paste photo

Those who joined in the cheer

_____ _____ _____
_____ _____ _____
_____ _____ _____
_____

Special events of the Holiday Season _____
_____
_____
_____
_____
_____
_____
_____
_____
_____

Memories of the past year _____

_____

_____

_____

_____

_____

_____

_____

_____

_____

_____

_____

_____

_____

_____

We exchanged greetings with our friends

paste Christmas card

Christmas _____

We gathered at _____

paste photo

Those who joined in the cheer

_____   _____   _____
_____   _____   _____
_____   _____   _____
_____   _____   _____

Special events of the Holiday Season _____
_____
_____
_____
_____
_____
_____
_____
_____

Memories of the past year _____

_____

_____

_____

_____

_____

_____

_____

_____

_____

_____

_____

_____

_____

_____

We exchanged greetings with our friends

paste Christmas card

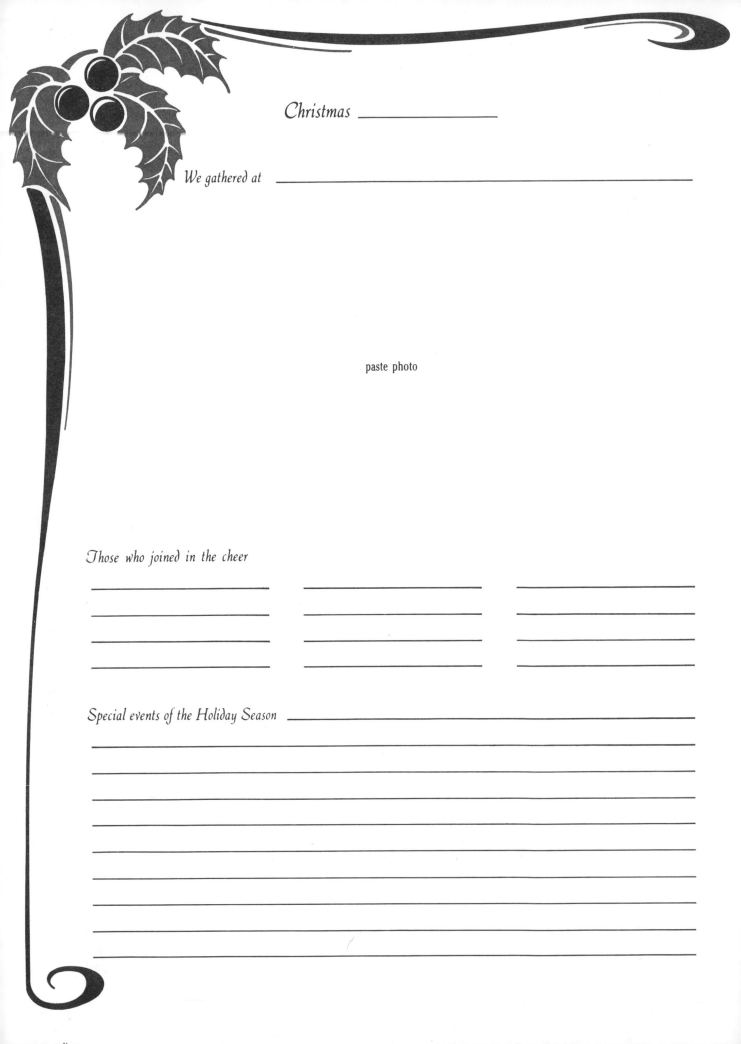

Christmas _____

We gathered at _____

paste photo

Those who joined in the cheer

_____   _____   _____
_____   _____   _____
_____   _____   _____
_____   _____   _____

Special events of the Holiday Season _____

_____
_____
_____
_____
_____
_____
_____
_____
_____

Memories of the past year _____

_____
_____
_____
_____
_____
_____
_____
_____
_____
_____
_____
_____
_____
_____

We exchanged greetings with our friends

paste Christmas card

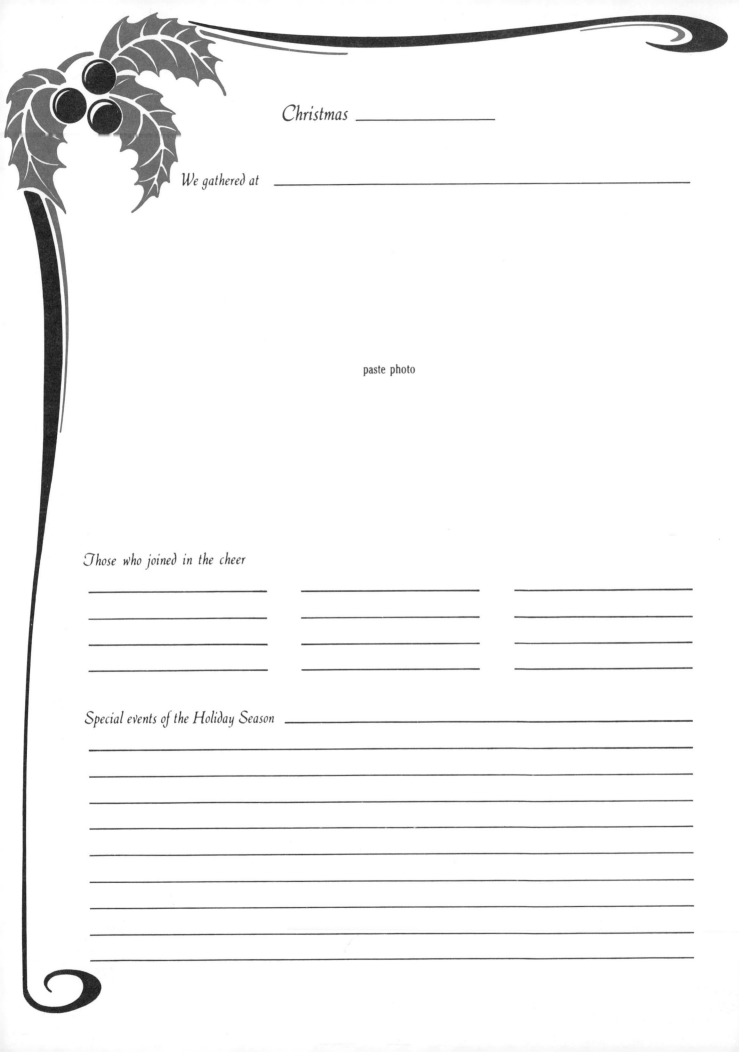

Christmas _____

We gathered at _____

paste photo

Those who joined in the cheer

_____   _____   _____
_____   _____   _____
_____   _____   _____
_____   _____   _____

Special events of the Holiday Season _____

_____
_____
_____
_____
_____
_____
_____
_____
_____

Memories of the past year _____

_____

_____

_____

_____

_____

_____

_____

_____

_____

_____

_____

_____

_____

_____

We exchanged greetings with our friends

paste Christmas card

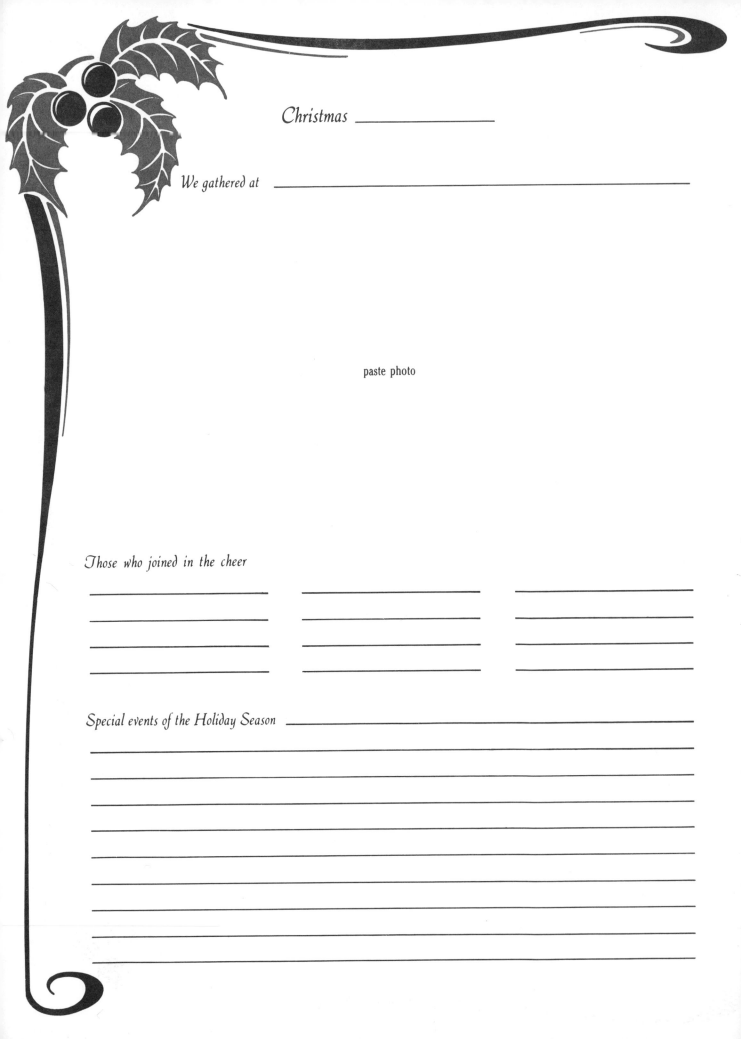

Christmas _____

We gathered at _____

paste photo

Those who joined in the cheer

_____ _____ _____
_____ _____ _____
_____ _____ _____
_____ _____ _____

Special events of the Holiday Season _____

_____

_____

_____

_____

_____

_____

_____

_____

_____

Memories of the past year _____

_____

_____

_____

_____

_____

_____

_____

_____

_____

_____

_____

_____

_____

_____

We exchanged greetings with our friends

paste Christmas card

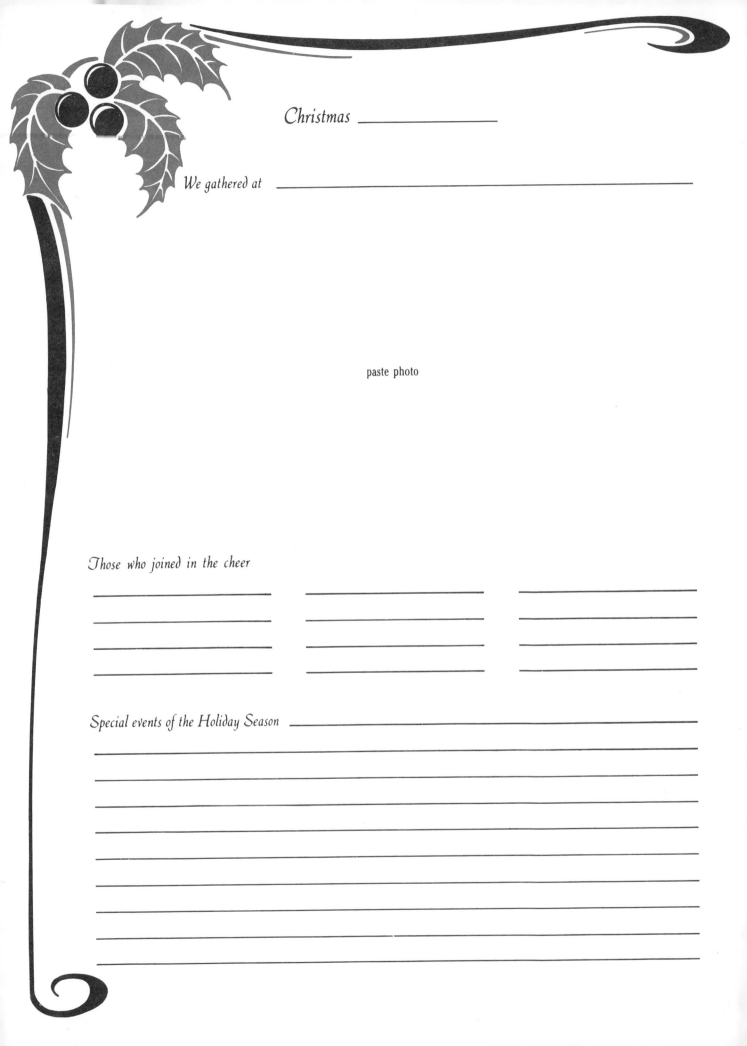

Christmas _____

We gathered at _____

paste photo

Those who joined in the cheer

_____ _____ _____
_____ _____ _____
_____ _____ _____
_____ _____ _____

Special events of the Holiday Season _____

_____

_____

_____

_____

_____

_____

_____

_____

_____

Memories of the past year _____

_____

_____

_____

_____

_____

_____

_____

_____

_____

_____

_____

_____

_____

_____

_____

_____

_____

We exchanged greetings with our friends

paste Christmas card

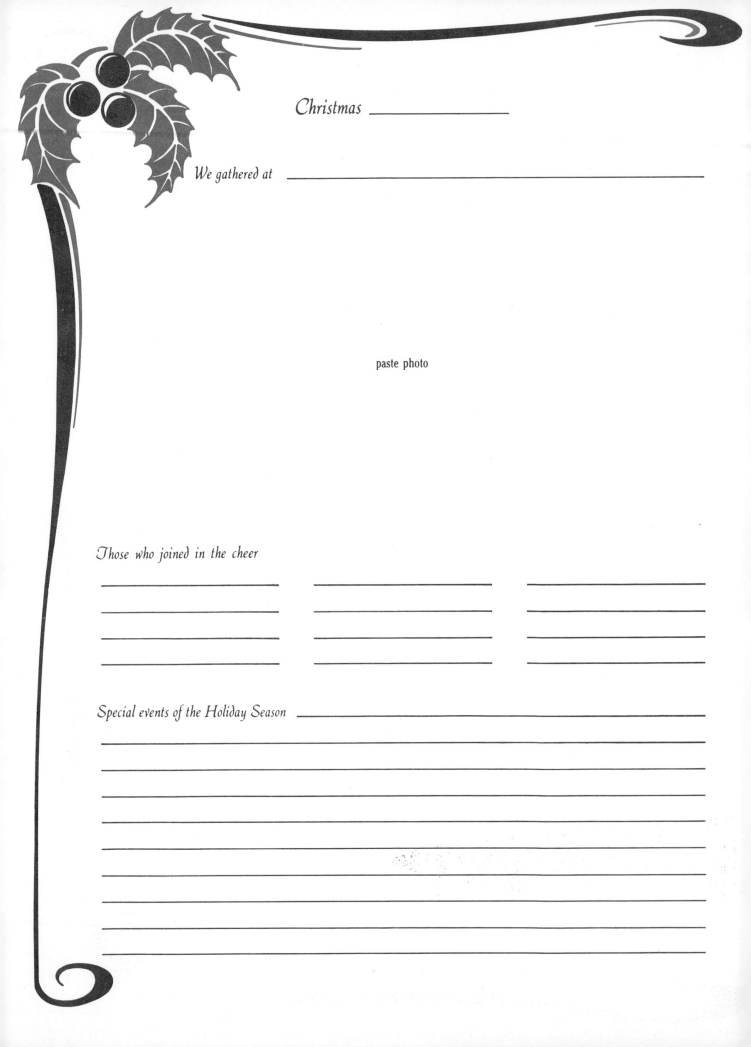

Christmas _____

We gathered at _____

paste photo

Those who joined in the cheer

_____   _____   _____
_____   _____   _____
_____   _____   _____
_____   _____   _____

Special events of the Holiday Season _____
_____
_____
_____
_____
_____
_____
_____
_____
_____
_____

Memories of the past year _____

_____

_____

_____

_____

_____

_____

_____

_____

_____

_____

_____

_____

_____

_____

_____

We exchanged greetings with our friends

paste Christmas card

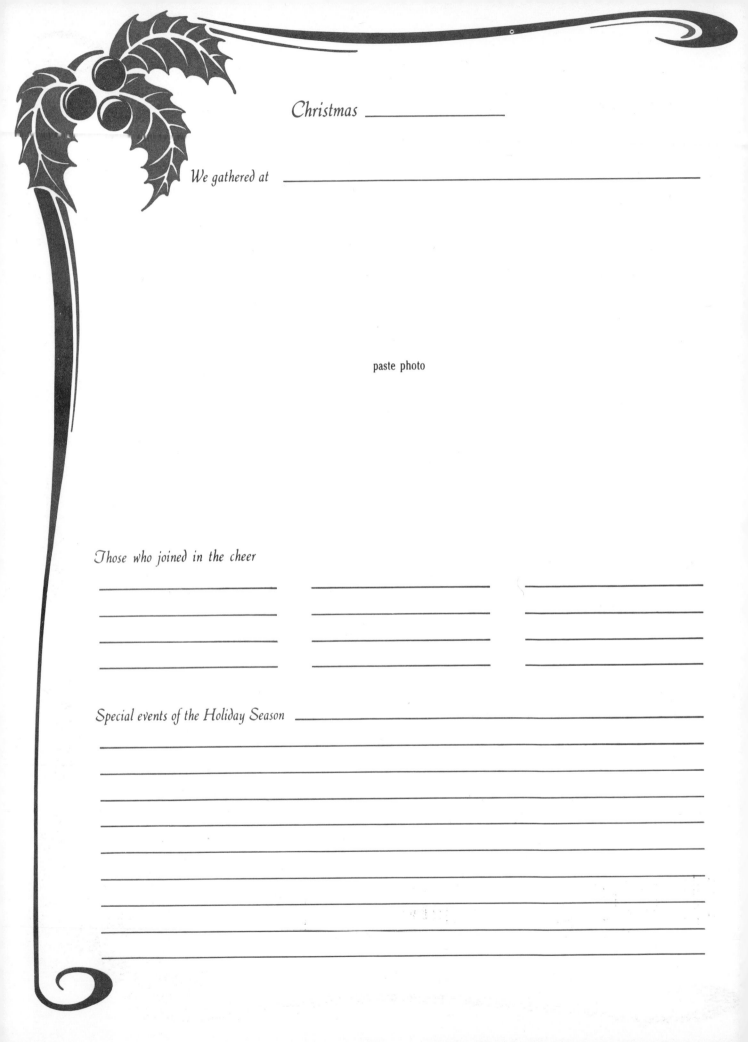

Christmas _____

We gathered at _____

paste photo

Those who joined in the cheer

_____   _____   _____
_____   _____   _____
_____   _____   _____
_____   _____   _____

Special events of the Holiday Season _____
_____
_____
_____
_____
_____
_____
_____
_____
_____
_____

Memories of the past year _____

_____

_____

_____

_____

_____

_____

_____

_____

_____

_____

_____

_____

_____

_____

_____

We exchanged greetings with our friends

paste Christmas card

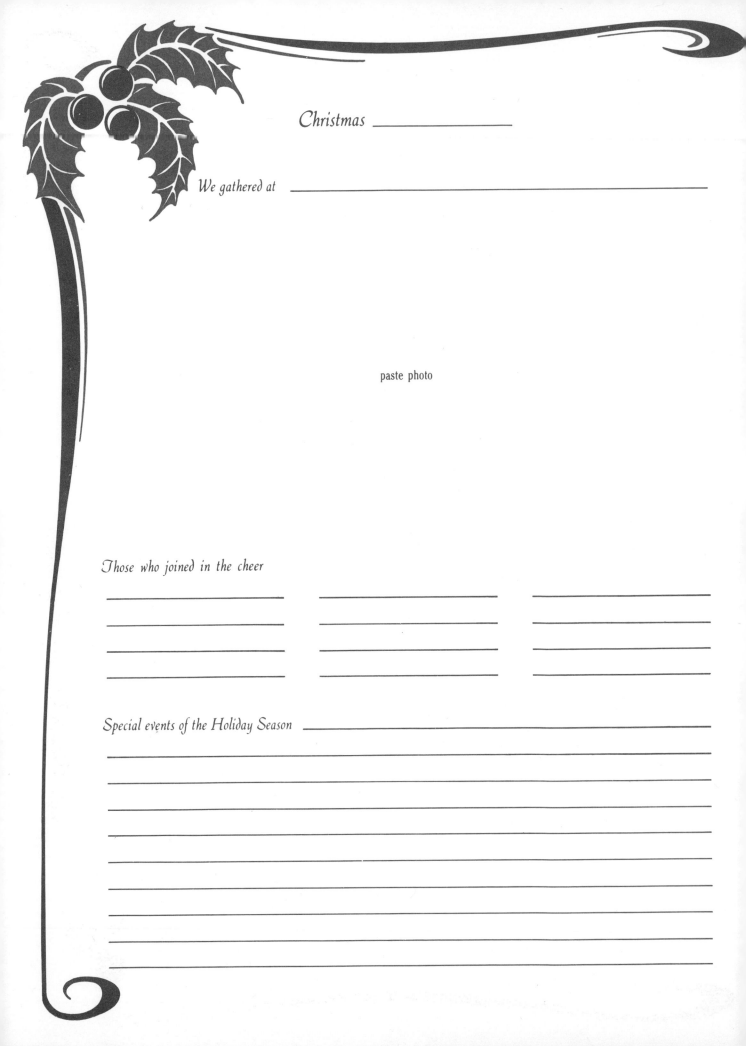

Christmas _____

We gathered at _____

paste photo

Those who joined in the cheer

_____   _____   _____
_____   _____   _____
_____   _____   _____
_____   _____   _____

Special events of the Holiday Season _____
_____
_____
_____
_____
_____
_____
_____
_____
_____

Memories of the past year _____

_____
_____
_____
_____
_____
_____
_____
_____
_____
_____
_____
_____

We exchanged greetings with our friends

paste Christmas card

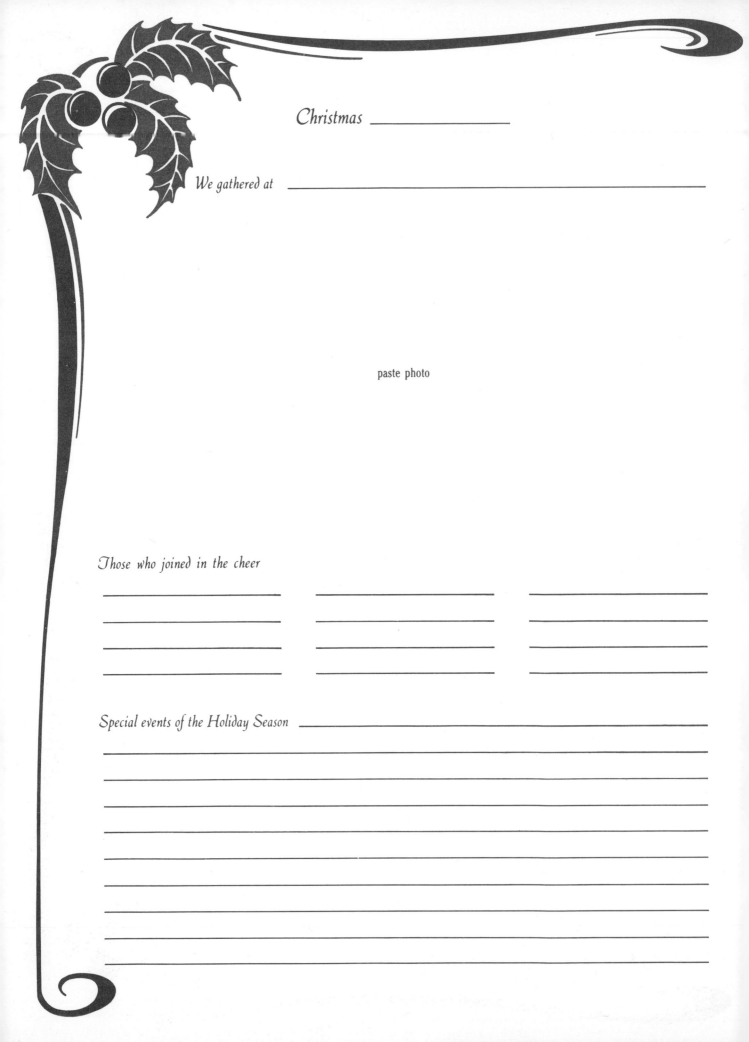

Christmas _____

We gathered at _____

paste photo

Those who joined in the cheer

_____   _____   _____
_____   _____   _____
_____   _____   _____
_____   _____   _____

Special events of the Holiday Season _____

_____

_____

_____

_____

_____

_____

_____

_____

Memories of the past year _____

_____

_____

_____

_____

_____

_____

_____

_____

_____

_____

_____

_____

_____

_____

We exchanged greetings with our friends

paste Christmas card

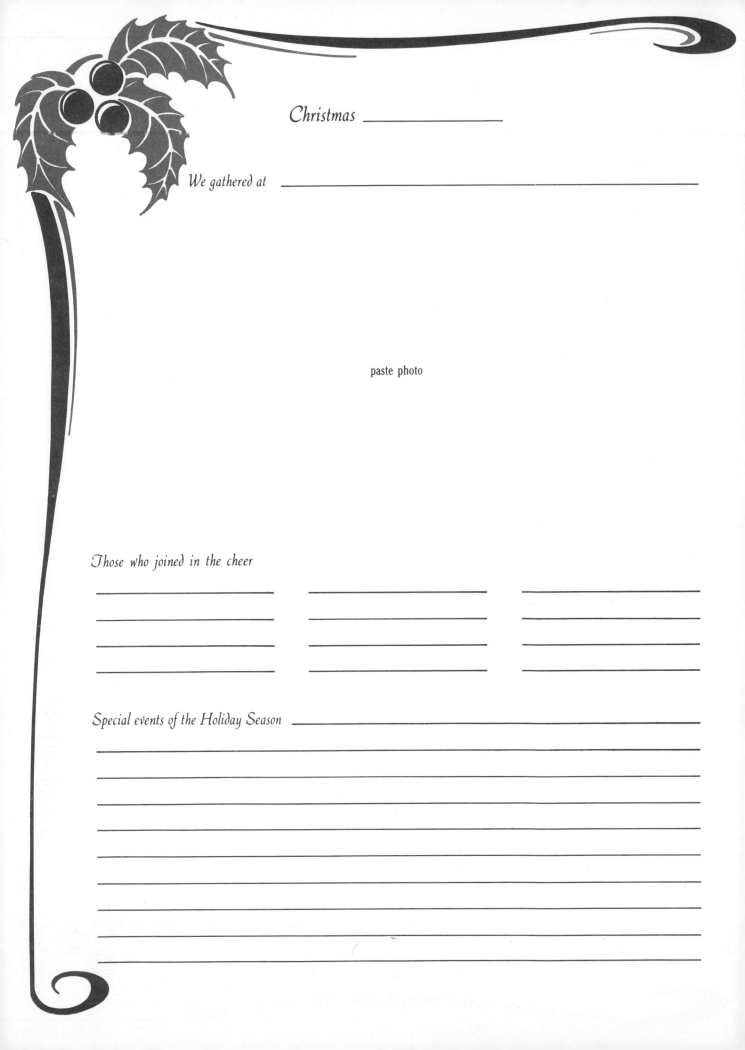

Christmas _____

We gathered at _____

paste photo

Those who joined in the cheer

_____ _____ _____
_____ _____ _____
_____ _____ _____
_____

Special events of the Holiday Season _____

_____
_____
_____
_____
_____
_____
_____
_____
_____
_____

Memories of the past year _____

_____
_____
_____
_____
_____
_____
_____
_____
_____
_____
_____
_____
_____
_____
_____

We exchanged greetings with our friends

paste Christmas card

Christmas _____

We gathered at _____

paste photo

Those who joined in the cheer

_____   _____   _____
_____   _____   _____
_____   _____   _____
_____   _____   _____
_____

Special events of the Holiday Season _____
_____
_____
_____
_____
_____
_____
_____
_____
_____
_____

Memories of the past year _____

_____

_____

_____

_____

_____

_____

_____

_____

_____

_____

_____

_____

_____

_____

_____

We exchanged greetings with our friends

paste Christmas card

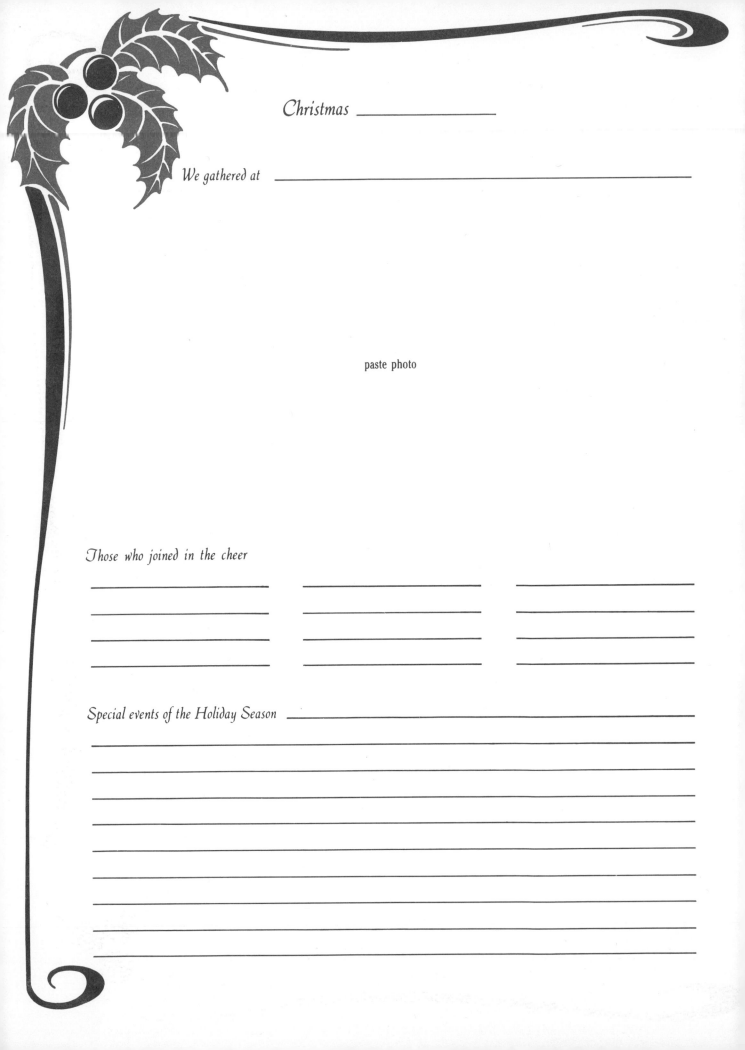

Christmas _____

We gathered at _____

paste photo

Those who joined in the cheer

_____   _____   _____
_____   _____   _____
_____   _____   _____
_____   _____   _____

Special events of the Holiday Season _____
_____
_____
_____
_____
_____
_____
_____
_____
_____

Memories of the past year _____

_____
_____
_____
_____
_____
_____
_____
_____
_____
_____
_____
_____
_____

We exchanged greetings with our friends

paste Christmas card

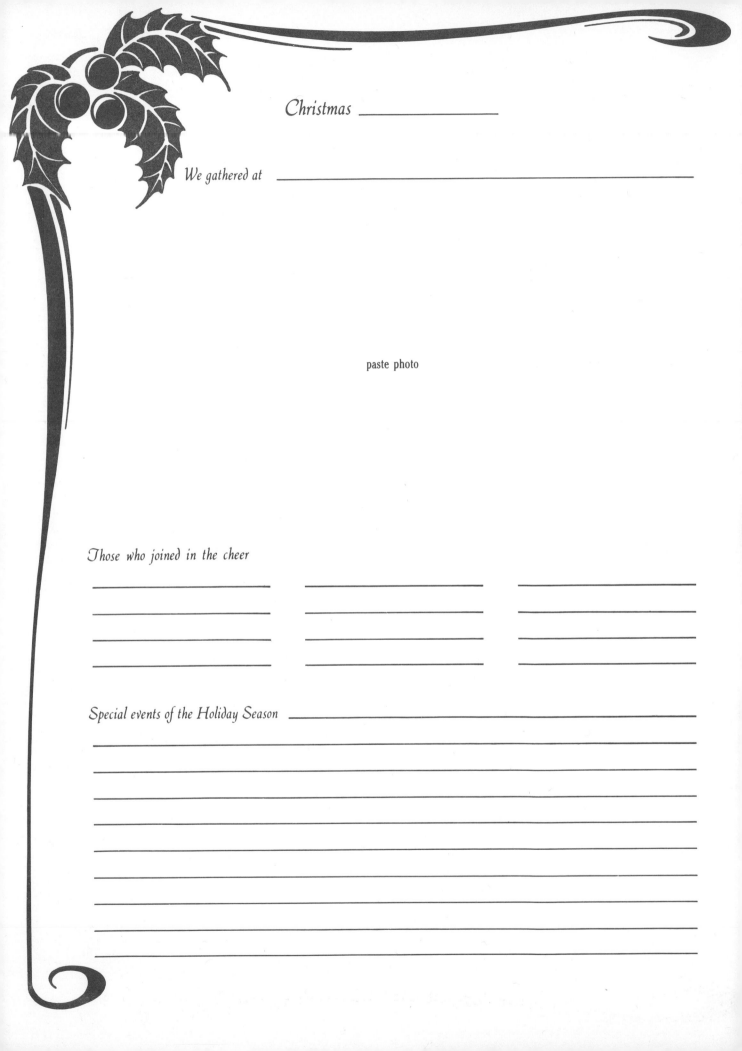

Christmas _____

We gathered at _____

paste photo

Those who joined in the cheer

_____   _____   _____
_____   _____   _____
_____   _____   _____
_____   _____   _____

Special events of the Holiday Season _____

_____
_____
_____
_____
_____
_____
_____
_____
_____

Memories of the past year _____

_____

_____

_____

_____

_____

_____

_____

_____

_____

_____

_____

_____

_____

_____

_____

_____

We exchanged greetings with our friends

paste Christmas card

Christmas _____

We gathered at _____

paste photo

Those who joined in the cheer

_____ _____ _____
_____ _____ _____
_____ _____ _____
_____

Special events of the Holiday Season _____
_____
_____
_____
_____
_____
_____
_____
_____

Memories of the past year _____

_____

_____

_____

_____

_____

_____

_____

_____

_____

_____

_____

_____

_____

_____

We exchanged greetings with our friends

paste Christmas card

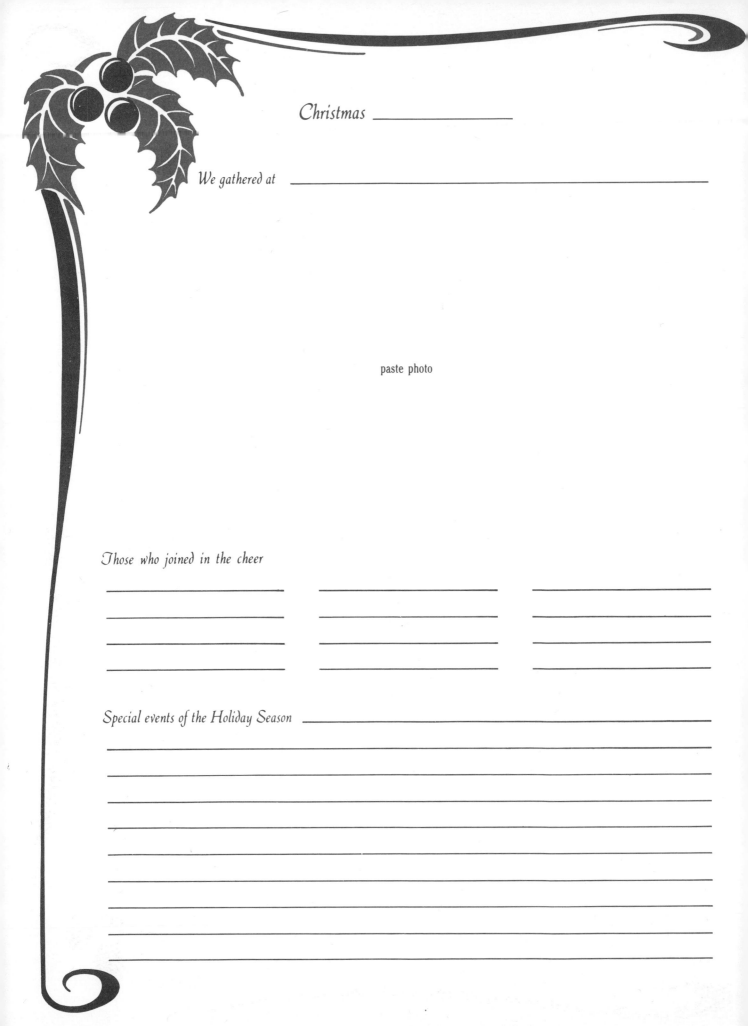

Christmas _____

We gathered at _____

paste photo

Those who joined in the cheer

_____ _____ _____
_____ _____ _____
_____ _____ _____
_____ _____ _____

Special events of the Holiday Season _____

_____
_____
_____
_____
_____
_____
_____
_____
_____
_____

Memories of the past year _____

_____

_____

_____

_____

_____

_____

_____

_____

_____

_____

_____

_____

_____

_____

_____

We exchanged greetings with our friends

paste Christmas card

Christmas _____

We gathered at _____

paste photo

Those who joined in the cheer

_____   _____   _____
_____   _____   _____
_____   _____   _____
_____   _____   _____

Special events of the Holiday Season _____

_____
_____
_____
_____
_____
_____
_____
_____
_____

Memories of the past year _____

_____

_____

_____

_____

_____

_____

_____

_____

_____

_____

_____

_____

_____

_____

We exchanged greetings with our friends

paste Christmas card

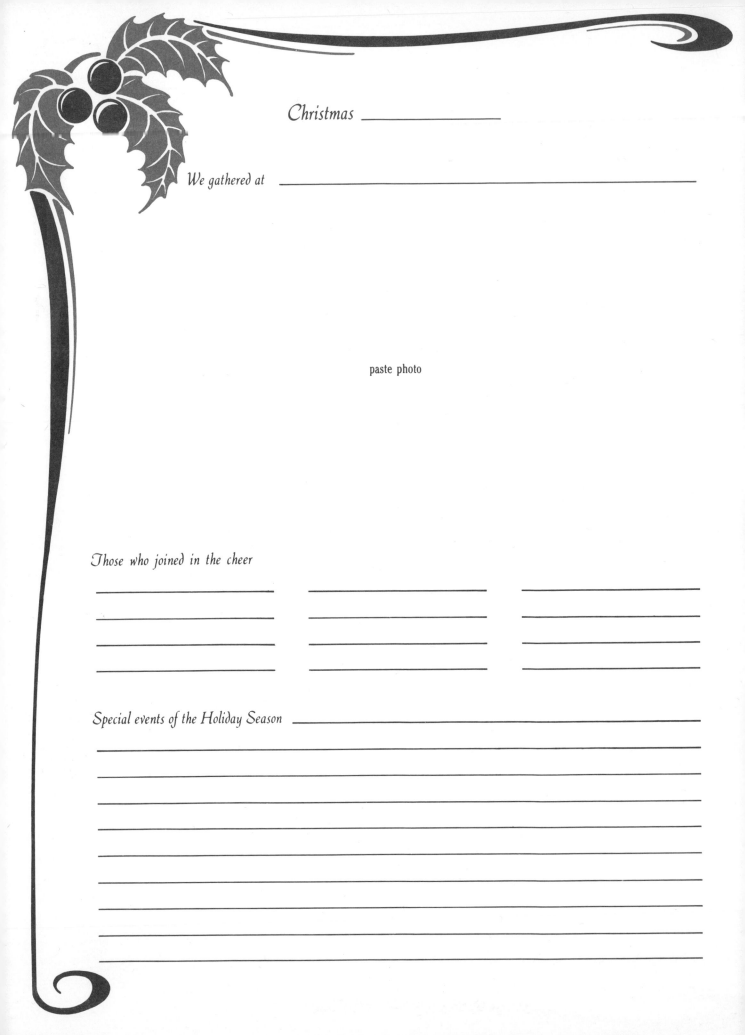

Christmas _____

We gathered at _____

paste photo

Those who joined in the cheer

_____ _____ _____
_____ _____ _____
_____ _____ _____
_____

Special events of the Holiday Season _____
_____
_____
_____
_____
_____
_____
_____
_____

Memories of the past year _____

_____

_____

_____

_____

_____

_____

_____

_____

_____

_____

_____

_____

_____

_____

_____

_____

_____

_____

_____

We exchanged greetings with our friends

paste Christmas card

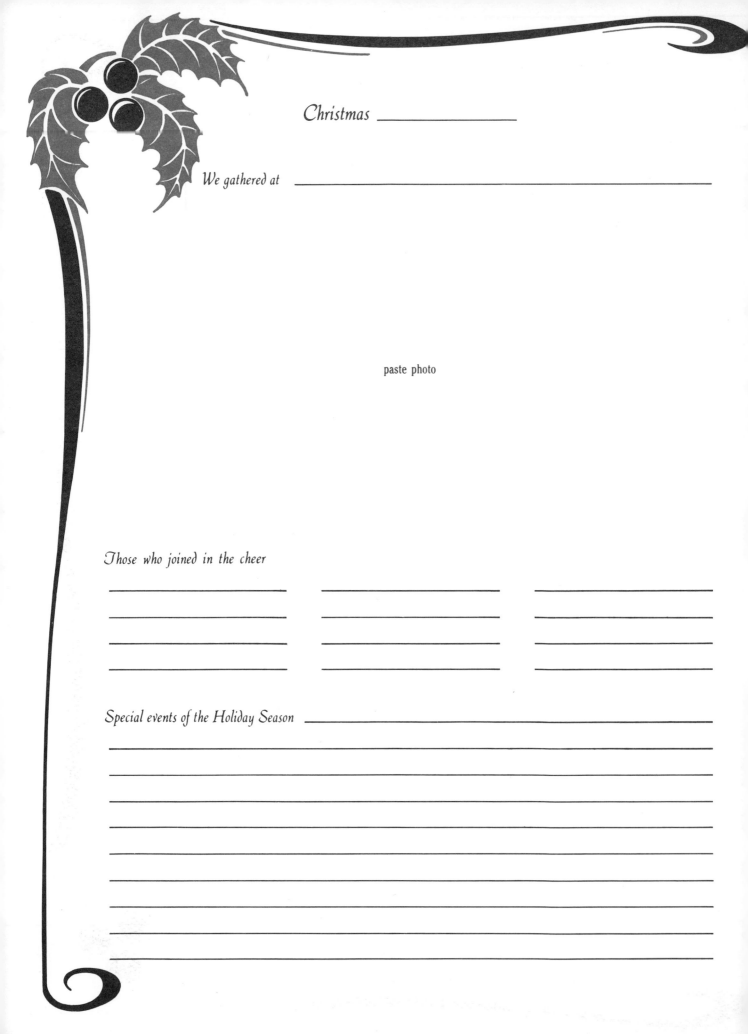

Christmas _____

We gathered at _____

paste photo

Those who joined in the cheer

_____ _____ _____
_____ _____ _____
_____ _____ _____
_____ _____ _____

Special events of the Holiday Season _____

_____
_____
_____
_____
_____
_____
_____
_____
_____

Memories of the past year _____

_____

_____

_____

_____

_____

_____

_____

_____

_____

_____

_____

_____

_____

_____

We exchanged greetings with our friends

paste Christmas card

Christmas _____

We gathered at _____

paste photo

Those who joined in the cheer

_____ _____ _____
_____ _____ _____
_____ _____ _____
_____ _____ _____

Special events of the Holiday Season _____
_____
_____
_____
_____
_____
_____
_____
_____
_____

Memories of the past year _____

_____

_____

_____

_____

_____

_____

_____

_____

_____

_____

_____

_____

_____

_____

We exchanged greetings with our friends

paste Christmas card

Christmas _____

We gathered at _____

paste photo

Those who joined in the cheer

_____ _____ _____
_____ _____ _____
_____ _____ _____
_____ _____ _____

Special events of the Holiday Season _____

_____
_____
_____
_____
_____
_____
_____
_____
_____

Memories of the past year _____

_____

_____

_____

_____

_____

_____

_____

_____

_____

_____

_____

_____

_____

We exchanged greetings with our friends

paste Christmas card

Christmas _____

We gathered at _____

paste photo

Those who joined in the cheer

_____ _____ _____
_____ _____ _____
_____ _____ _____
_____ _____ _____

Special events of the Holiday Season _____

_____

_____

_____

_____

_____

_____

_____

_____

_____

Memories of the past year _____

_____
_____
_____
_____
_____
_____
_____
_____
_____
_____
_____
_____
_____

We exchanged greetings with our friends

paste Christmas card

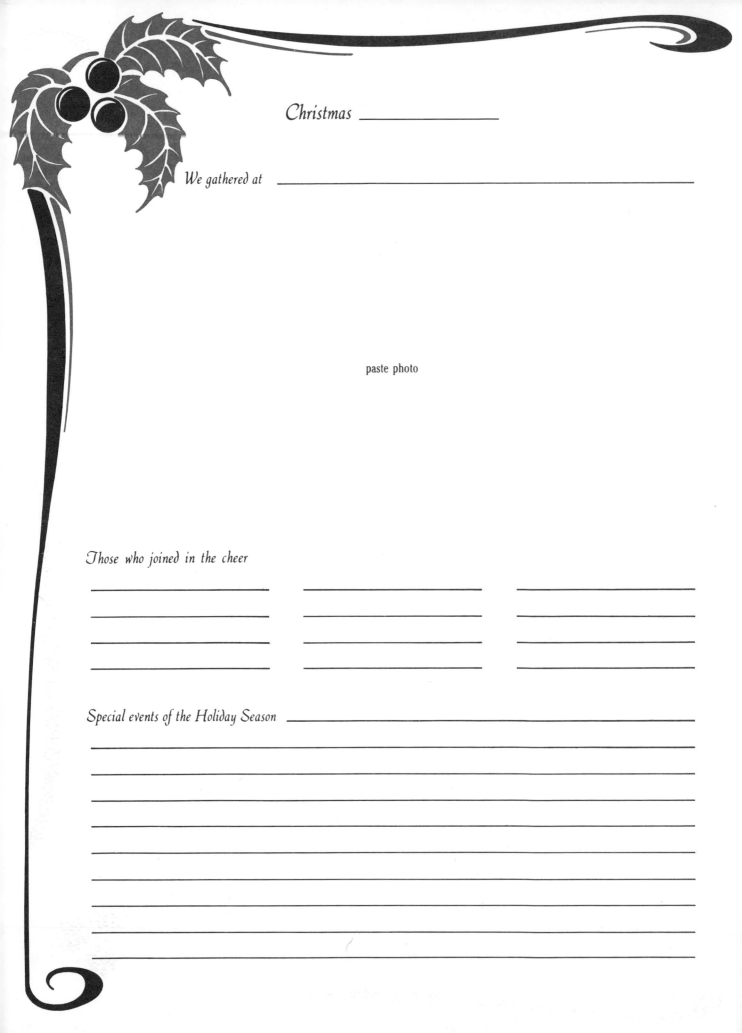

Christmas _____

We gathered at _____

paste photo

Those who joined in the cheer

_____   _____   _____
_____   _____   _____
_____   _____   _____
_____   _____   _____

Special events of the Holiday Season _____
_____
_____
_____
_____
_____
_____
_____
_____
_____

Memories of the past year _____

_____

_____

_____

_____

_____

_____

_____

_____

_____

_____

_____

_____

_____

_____

We exchanged greetings with our friends

paste Christmas card

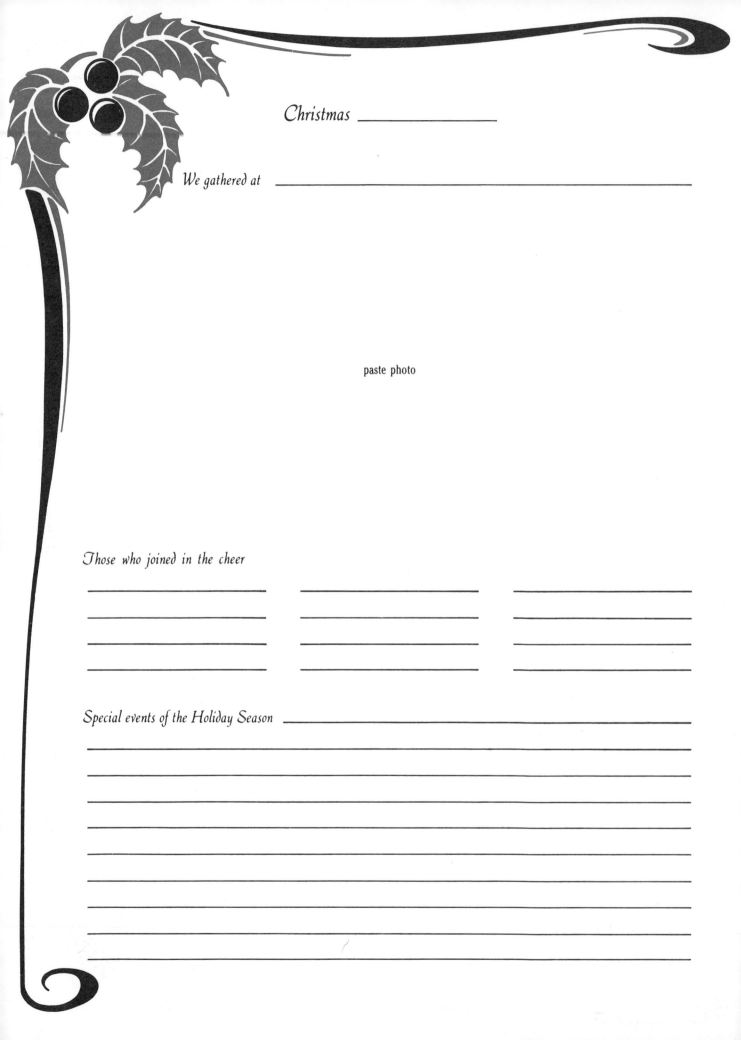

Christmas _____

We gathered at _____

paste photo

Those who joined in the cheer

_____ _____ _____
_____ _____ _____
_____ _____ _____
_____ _____ _____
_____ _____ _____

Special events of the Holiday Season _____

_____

_____

_____

_____

_____

_____

_____

_____

_____

Memories of the past year _____

_____

_____

_____

_____

_____

_____

_____

_____

_____

_____

_____

_____

_____

We exchanged greetings with our friends

paste Christmas card

Christmas _____

We gathered at _____

paste photo

Those who joined in the cheer

_____   _____   _____
_____   _____   _____
_____   _____   _____
_____   _____   _____

Special events of the Holiday Season _____

_____

_____

_____

_____

_____

_____

_____

_____

_____

Memories of the past year _____

_____

_____

_____

_____

_____

_____

_____

_____

_____

_____

_____

_____

_____

_____

We exchanged greetings with our friends

paste Christmas card

Notes